MW00628474

cat

"Tom Lang's **cat** offers a deceptively deep and complex story in the guise of a simple tale about a reformed cat hater and his feline, Bouhaki. Lang paints his characters with deft strokes, sweetly hooking his unsuspecting reader's heart."

-Shannon Brownlee, Senior Editor,
U.S. News & World Report

eagle

"Absolutely hilarious! Lang has created a unique and clever look at eagles."

-Nicole Duclos, Alaska Raptor
Rehabilitation Center

"A brilliant mix of knowledge, humor and story-telling, **eagle** is a classic on the American Bald Eagle."

-Joe Ordonez, Alaskan nature
photographer and founder of
Rainbow Glacier Adventures,
Haines, Alaska

salmon

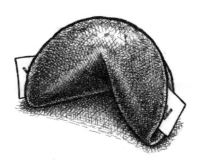

A Story by Tom Lang

Published by: BOUDELANG PRESS

P.O Box 3005

Venice, CA 90291-9998

TEL. 310.712.5606
WEBSITE: **www.boudelang.com**
E-mail BOUDELANG @aol.com

Illustration and Concept by Andrew Reidenbaugh

Design by Siobhan Burns

Editing by Laurie Insley

Production by Sandy Hubbard

Library of Congress Catalog Card Number 98-92895

ISBN 0-9649742-1-5

TO LAURIE
ONE OF THE CHOSEN

I'VE ALWAYS BEEN AN EMOTIONAL FISH. MY FRIENDS attribute my moods to my overly sensitive lateral lines, pores that run down my body from head to tail. These pores hook up with a canal under my skin that connects with my brain, helping me sense minute disturbances and subtle movement. That's how I pick the best current, swim through murky water and maintain the tight formation of my school.

1

But I think my sensitivity has more to do with unresolved issues from my troubled childhood. I'm an orphan. My mother and father died when I was conceived. I lived under a half-foot of gravel in Chilkat Lake for 6 months before I emerged from my alevin stage to become a fry. I fought for a year with my 4000 brothers and sisters over cheap crustaceans and microscopic algae slop—green desmids, blue diatoms and blue-green dinoflagellates. I huddled in fear of swim-by killings when the Chars, a gang of crazed fish high on zooplankton, wiped out 90 of my siblings in one swallow.

Only a few good salmon, a hundred or so from each family, are fortunate enough to survive to become smolts and head out to the saltwater. I was one of the proud, brave, and I suppose, lucky. I spent my years at sea dodging fishnets and battling an ocean of food-frenzied whales, sharks and sea lions. Many times I came within a scale's length of a brutal death from cruise ship rudders. Blown off course by cross currents, I still managed to travel over 2000 miles a year. The light at the end of this long Inside Passage was, of course, the happy spawning ground.

To spawn, to reproduce, is the ultimate goal for a salmon, a reward for a hard-fought life. A return to the spawning ground is a return to where we were born. Although I have never met a salmon that has spawned, fantasies of the spawning ground, a mysterious, sensual garden of delights, have danced in my brain for the last four years. I dreamed of mating with my special love, floating around the lake all day, joking with my buddies. Not a care in the world.

And, now, here I was, at the beginning of the last leg of my odyssey, treading water in front of a sign at the mouth of the Chilkat River that read:

CHILKAT LAKE

25 MILES

"HOME OF THE SPAWNING SOCKEYES"

SWIM SAFELY.

MY BUDDIES AND I WENT DOWN TO CELEBRATE OUR last day in saltwater at Sockeye Sushi, a bar and restaurant 100 feet below the surface of the Lynn Canal, right near the mouth of the Chilkat River. A banner outside the joint read, "Last Stop For Food." Inside, Fry and the Fingerlings sang "Let's Spawn 'Til Dawn" on the jukebox.

There was Milt, who was originally from a rival school before he transferred over to us last month when his entire graduating class was kidnapped near Juneau and never heard from again. Milt and I hit it off right away, as if we had known each other our entire life-cycle. Some fish mistook us for brothers and couldn't tell us apart.

Alevin was the brain of our school, a graduate of the Migratory School of Limnology, the study of lakes, ponds, streams and the life they contain.

Gill, on the other fin, was an airhead and a paranoid hypochondriac. He ranted on and on about a global conspiracy to capture all of us Sockeye and ship us off to foreign lands in cans and jars. Whatever you say, Gill.

We had covered over 20 miles that day and we were starved. We polished off a platter of arrow worms, a bowl of bivalve larvae, 12 orders of snails, 3 mixed invertebrate plates and 10 Alaskan amphipod rolls. While I squiggled over to the All-You-Can-Eat-Kelp-Bed, the fellas started their usual arguments. Want to get a school of salmon riled up? Ask them how we can possibly migrate thousands of miles and still find our way back to the spot where we were born.

"What I'm trying to tell you boys," Milt said, chewing on an ostrocod, "is that it's all smell. We've got a half million receptors per square inch up our noses. We follow the scent, baby. It's as simple as that."

"No way, Milt," Gill said, spacing out for a minute as he watched the air bubbles from his mouth float to the surface. "It's electricity, man. See, as ocean currents travel across the earth's magnetic field, electricity is created and we pick up those signals with our lateral lines. Takes us home. If THEY don't get us first."

"Gill, you've got the brain of a copepod," Al said, pushing his glasses up the bridge of his pectoral fin. "Our cycle is planted deep inside, imprinted on our chromosomes. Our homing ability is an inherited response to our environment."

"Hey, Red, what do you say?" Milt said to me as I swam back from the kelp buffet with a plate piled high with *Fucus, Porphyra* and *Nereocystis*.

"I don't care how we get there," I said, sucking in a strand of *Ulva*, "I just want to get upstream and start spawning."

"Here, here!" the boys cheered, raising their cups of Vin du Plankton, "to spawning!"

"Listen," I said, tilting my snout toward the jukebox. King Chinook was singing a bluesy version of "Hate Being Late to Mate Your Date." We rocked back and forth, lip-synching to the song.

"YOU ARE ONE OF THE CHOSEN."

I didn't sleep well that night, flipping and flopping, jumping out of the water a few times. I dreamed of my deceased mentor, the great holy fish, the Dolly Salmon, who lived in exile underneath a kelp bed until he was tragically crushed to death by bags of garbage thrown into the ocean from a cruise ship.

I met the Dolly when I was still a smolt, not more than three or four inches long. Our

9

currents crossed the day I had my first brush with the Sea Monster, the Humpback whale.

I've never been fond of whales. They're fat gluttons who think they're so smart. If they are so intelligent, how come they sing the same stupid song over and over again?

So, there I was, on my first day at sea, when a whale opened his mouth and started sucking in hundreds of my people, along with herring, snappers and part of an oil slick. I watched from a safe distance, out of his current of death. I got steamed and swam up along side him, staring him straight in his left eye.

"Hey, fat boy," I said, "I'm not always going to be this small. The next time we meet, you're mine."

The whale gave me a smirk and went off humming his annoying tune. I whacked him on his side with my tail and took off to catch up with what was left of my school.

"Psssssst."

I swished my tail, looking behind me.

"Pssssst, down here."

I looked down and saw an old salmon peeking out from a kelp bed. I dove down to get a closer look.

"Hello, Sockeye," he said.

"Uh, hello...ah..."

"I am the Dolly Salmon. I will be your mentor."

"Hmmm...mentor. And what does that mean, exactly?" I asked, a little suspect of this old salmon of the sea.

"I will tell you things."

"Such as?"

"You are one of the chosen."

"Sounds like a fortune cookie I read last week at Swim Lo's."

"It is your fortune, Sockeye."

"Oh, yeah? Okay, thank you, I guess. What else?"

"Swim swiftly."

"Swim swiftly? Thanks for the tip, Dolly, but I have to get going."

"Sockeye?"

"Yeah?"

"To the blind, all things are sudden."

"Gotcha. Later."

I swam off, but as odd as he was, something about him stuck with me.

And now, the night before the last leg of my journey, he appeared to me in a dream.

"You are one of the chosen," he repeated from years ago. *"It is your destiny and purpose."*

"Whatever," I said, turning to go.

Suddenly empty bottles, tin cans and dirty napkins poured down from above, burying the Dolly Salmon.

"SPAWNING GROUND! SPAWNING GROUND! Spawning Ground!"

I awoke to the chanting rumble of thousands of salmon swarming at the starting line of the Spawn Marathon, the endurance race to the spawning ground. I joined the fellas and wiggled my way into place at the mouth of the river.

"Spawning Ground! Spawning Ground! Spawning Ground!"

I felt pressure on my tail fin.

"Hey, watch your snout, pal," I snapped at a sockeye behind me.

"SPAWNING GROUND! SPAWNING GROUND! SPAWNING GROUND!"

Every salmon was pumped. Thousands of gills pulsed the water with their short, deep breaths.

The race official dropped his dorsal fin and the race was on. We pushed, wiggled and squiggled. We were still in the saltwater, but a hint of fresh water tickled my gills, flickering something primordial in my brain. I flipped my tail and jumped ahead of the fish in front of me. I felt good.

"Watch out! Net!" Al yelled. "Dive!"

Instinctively I let the air out of my swim bladder and dove to the bottom for safety, the sound waves of my captive brothers vibrating through the water as the net dragged them toward the surface. My nose banged into the silty bottom. I fluttered my tail to balance myself and to gather my wits. Al and Milt were beside me. But where was Gill?

"Who's paranoid now?" Gill hollered.

We looked up. Gill stared down at us from the netted mass of salmon, rising above us like a storm cloud. I was staring helplessly at the surface when I heard a laugh and turned to see a couple of flounder feeding on the bottom. They were smiling.

"Good luck, salmies," one flounder yelled.

"Yeah, you'll need it," said the other.

I surged toward them but Al stopped me.

"Let it go, Red, they're not worth it. They're bottom feeders."

I'D WITNESSED MANY SLAUGHTERS AND I'D LOST many friends over the years, but it never gets easier. We quickly recited the 23rd Salmon Psalm for Gill and regrouped.

We continued upstream, into the dark current. I was back in the fresh water for the first time since I was a youngster. I thought I would miss the salt, but I felt good, healthier without it. We fought the downstream current as it shoved us off our rhythm, slamming us back against the rocks lying in the river. We pulled over after a few hours to catch our breath.

"Want anything to eat?" I said, watching a gaggle of cladocerans crawl by us.

"Never thought I'd turn down a fresh water crustacean, but, no, I'm not hungry," Milt said.

"Me, neither," I said.

"You guys," Al said, "we salmon don't eat anymore once we enter the fresh water. There are a couple of other things you both should know—"

"Not now, professor," I said, anxious to push on with our pilgrimage.

We continued up the Chilkat until the last light of day faded deep behind the mountains. We stopped in an eddy and curled up for the night while Al put us to bed with a hot little story about a sexy female salmon.

"She digs a spot for her eggs in water

about 12 inches deep with a surface current 18 inches per second, slow enough so the eggs aren't washed away. The hole itself is between 4 to 12 inches. Then she buries the fertilized eggs in 6 inches of gravel. She'll lay thousands of eggs, but that's nothing compared to the female mola mola, the 9-foot-long sunfish whose giant ovaries contain 300 million eggs and—"

"Enough!" I said, fanning myself with a fin. "Is it just me or is this river heating up?"

"Must be an aquifer bubbling up around here, cause my temperature's rising," Milt said.

"Hard to get any sleep around here with stories like that, Al," I said.

"Sweet dreams, boys," Al said, chuckling.

"Thanks, Al."

I WAS IN THE MIDDLE OF A LARGE LAKEBED. *Thousands of salmon swam below me as I floated along the surface. There were tiny alevins, small fry, larger smolts and full-grown adults. The Dolly Salmon appeared next to me. He had a plastic ring from a six-pack container wrapped around his neck and a piece of Styrofoam stuck in his tail fin.*

"That's my cousin, Coho, and my distant

relative, Humpy, and Uncle Silver," I said, looking down as we scooted across the water. "Wait a minute, there's Gill. Where are we, Dolly Salmon"?

"This is the Spawned Beyond, Sockeye. Every salmon passes through here."

"I'll be here someday, I suppose."

"Someday," the Dolly said.

"But, not for awhile, I've got a lot of business to take care of, you know."

The Dolly Salmon nodded his head, smiled and said, "Sockeye—"

SOMETHING SHARP LIKE CORAL TORE AT MY SIDE AND
ripped me awake.

"Bear! Bear! Swim for your lives!" I yelled.

The bear stomped into the water, his big
furry paw slapping for me again. I faked left,
then shot back right. Water was splashing
everywhere. Fish were flopping and flying
into each other, trying to escape. Pain
streaked from snout to tail as I scooted away
from the bear. I stopped and looked around.

Milt, his eyes the size of oyster shells, circled a pair of eyeglasses lying on the river bottom.

"Where's Al, Red? Where's Al?"

I squinted up through the murky water and saw the hairy beast on the shore, leaning into the river, Al in his claws. As the bear opened his mouth, I accelerated through the water, timed my jump and leaped into the air, biting down hard on the paw holding Al. The bear roared and reared up, but he refused to loosen his grip on my friend. I fell on the gravel bar and quickly wiggled back into the water. I swung around in time to see the bear's mouth close over Al's head.

I treaded water for a moment, my mind frozen in denial. Then I swam away in grief, memories of a shark attack that killed friends of my family flashing through my brain—another act of senseless violence against the Sockeye salmon.

"ARE YOUR TEETH GROWING LONGER, IS YOUR JAW elongating, your snout hooking, your back humping, your skin thickening and your body absorbing your scales, or are you just happy to see me?"

"Excuse me?"

"Hi, I'm Ova."

She was a pretty girl with a big belly.

"I'm Red. Big Red."

A couple of male salmon swam close

25

to Ova, giving her the once over. I lunged and snapped at them.

"Sorrrrrry," one of them said as they headed upstream.

Ova giggled and turned a deep shade of salmon pink. Then she looked at me with concern.

"You're bleeding."

"Oh...yeah." With all that had happened I'd forgotten that the bear had cut me.

"Your operculum appears to be damaged."

"What?"

"Oh, I'm sorry," she said, "your operculum, your gill cover. I'm a crash unit nurse over at the Saturday Night Salmon Fights."

She flippered over to me and gave me a quick exam.

"It's just a scale wound," she said, "you're fine."

"So are you," I said.

She flushed a deeper shade of red and gave

me a little swat with her tail.

"I think the fresh water is going to your head," she said, with a twinkle in her eye. "You don't know me well enough to talk to me like that."

"But I like to talk to you like that," I said.

"Then you should get to know me better."

"Well, how about—"

"I'll be up in Chilkat Lake," she said, spinning around to go. I watched her tail swish gently back and forth as she headed upstream.

"Hello, Dolly."

"Hello, Sockeye."

We were again floating above the Spawned Beyond. In the middle of the sea of salmon I saw a familiar face.

"There's Al," I said.

"Yes, Sockeye."

"Al's dead."

"In some ways, Sockeye."

"What's he waiting for in that line?"

29

"That's the line for the Reincarnation Debarkation Station."

"What do you get there?"

"Your reward."

"Reward? Great. He didn't even get to spawn. It better be a good reward."

"Your reward is fulfilling your destiny and purpose, Sockeye," the Dolly Salmon said as he nodded and smiled.

"Wow, I'm sure glad I'm chosen, right, Dolly"?

"Sockeye," the Dolly Salmon said, "there is something you must know—"

Suddenly, paper plates, cups, beer bottles and animal bones descended through the water, blurring my connection with the Dolly Salmon.

I DIDN'T FEEL GOOD. I WAS TIRED ALL THE TIME. I FELT like I had a chronic case *of Saprolegnia Parasitica*, the deadly white furry moss that is fatal to salmon. I hadn't eaten in days and I was bruised and beaten from bouncing off rocks while fighting the downstream current.

But Milt and I pushed on.

We reached the confluence of the Chilkat and Tsirku rivers and instinctively took a left and started up the Tsirku delta. The water was shallow and the current slower. The gravel rubbed my belly as I moved upstream.

"What's that?" I said.

"Sounds like music," Milt said.

We slowed down, the sound of singing echoing through the water, vibrating my lateral lines.

"Over there," Milt said, motioning with his snout.

A school of smolts on their way out to sea surfed on the downstream flow. They were young, fresh and full of promise, their whole lives in front of them. As they swam closer and looked over at us, their eyes bulged out of their sockets.

"Aaaaaaaaah! Look at those teeth! The hump on his back! No scales! Aaaaaaaah!"

I looked around. There was no one behind me. Were they talking about me? The smolts scattered off to another channel, screaming and yelling.

"How do I look?" I asked Milt.

"Uh, well, you look…great, Red," Milt said, leaning against a gravel bar, breathing heavily.

"Well, I don't see why they were so afraid of me, Milt. If your teeth get any longer you could pass for a beaver."

"I was trying to be polite, Red, but since you asked, the bigger the hump on your back gets the more you look like a killer shark."

"Hey, that's a cheap shot, Milt. The way your head is turning green doesn't exactly—"

"What are we fighting for, Red?" Milt said. "We need to conserve our energy. Look, let's take this shallow channel. It'll be easier."

I followed Milt up the thin stream, my body half out of the water. Milt picked up speed and pulled ahead of me, not noticing a sharp turn in the channel.

"Wheeeeeeee!" Milt yelled.

"Watch out, Milt, slow down!"

Milt missed the turn and beached himself

on a gravel bar. He squirmed and squiggled trying to get himself back into the water.

"C'mon, Milt," I hollered, "you look silly."

"Just a second, Red," Milt said, "I'm almost there."

First I thought it was a cloud covering the sun as a shadow fell over us. But when I heard the flutter in the wind, followed by a high-pitched wail, I knew it was trouble. I watched in horror as an eagle snatched Milt in its talons and slowly struggled to drag him off the ground.

"Hey! Drop him!" I screamed at the eagle as I jumped out of the water, bouncing toward them. The eagle tried to gain momentum for lift off but I pushed out of the water and bit it on the wing. The eagle crashed and shifted Milt to its left talon, attacking my neck with its beak. Then the bird of prey sliced its right talon across my stomach, knocking me back onto the gravel bar and pinning me to the ground with its talon.

"We got a problem here?" the eagle said. "Stick around, I'll be back."

With Milt still in its grasp the eagle furiously flapped his wings. I tried to get up but the lack of water and loss of blood weakened me. I squiggled on the gravel bar while I watched my last friend fade into the sky. The cold and darkness smothered me.

"Do you know your name?"

"Uh, yeah...uh, Red."

"Do you know what year of your lifecycle you're in?"

"Um...fourth, no, fifth."

"Do you know where you're going?"

"Uh...why, are you lost?"

I was floating in shallow water. Ova was tending to me.

"I remember being dragged from the

37

gravel bar. I thought it was the eagle coming back for me. I didn't have any strength to fight him. But it was you."

"Here, have some more water," Ova said, as she pulled me further into the stream. She was applying pressure to different parts of me with her fins.

"How do you feel, Red?" she said.

"Never felt better. A fish net took my friend Gill, a bear ate Al and an eagle just took off with Milt. Myself, I feel like I've been run through the turbines of a dam. Looks like a win-win to me."

"Well, you're alive. Your airway is open, your breathing is restored and your circulation is maintained. I think I've stopped the bleeding. You were in shock."

"Shock?"

"Yes, you were chilled, breathing harshly, nauseous, clammy and pale."

"And how do I look now?"

"You look…ah…ah…better. More important is how you feel."

"I wish I felt as good as you look."

Ova's body reddened, her head glittering with a hint of green.

"You're obviously feeling better, Red, and your bleeding has stopped. But you should rest for the night and recover your strength. I have to go. The entrance to Chilkat Lake is just around the bend. Why don't you come up and get to know me better."

She gave me a smooch with her big lips and swished away.

AFTER OVA LEFT, I FLOATED ALONE WITH MY thoughts. Here I was, just a few strokes away from my destination, the end of my journey. The Happy Spawning Grounds. Party Time.

But everyone I'd spent my life with was dead, and, by all rights, I should be dead as well. Why had I been spared?

I wondered about Ova. What part did she play in my journey? Why did she appear whenever I needed help?

Because I was one of the chosen! That's why. Now the Dolly Salmon's words made sense. I had been chosen to spawn.

And spawn I would.

Everyday I would spawn in memory of my fallen brothers. I would name my first 100 sons Gill, the next 100 Al, the next 100 Milt. Every morning, while Ova and I served them fresh algae, I would tell the kids about their namesakes. They would have the father I never had. Of course, the day would come when our kids would be ready to go out to sea by themselves and we'd hope we had empowered them with enough knowledge to help them live fulfilling lives in the deep. Then Ova and I would curl up and retire in a corner of Chilkat Lake and wait for their return.

I had a big job ahead of me and, as Ova said, I needed my rest for the last of my quest. I settled into the water and let sleep lap over me.

I SWAM EFFORTLESSLY UPSTREAM, FULL OF VIGOR. The Dolly Salmon appeared beside me.

"Oh, great holy fish," I said to him, "I've lived my whole life by instinct, gone with the flow, never questioned much. And now, as I near my home after all these years and obstacles, I feel confident about my ability to fulfill my destiny and purpose."

The Dolly Salmon nodded his head, closed his eyes and smiled.

"But I have one last question for you, Dolly."

"Yes, Sockeye?"

"What do I do with my life after I spawn, oh, great denizen of the deep?"

The Dolly Salmon nodded his head again, closed his eyes and smiled.

"You die, Sockeye."

I shook my head to get the water out of my ears.

"Excuse me?"

"It is your gift to the universe."

"Really? Don't you think the universe has enough gifts? I planned on spawning the rest of the year."

"You spawn but once, Sockeye."

"Once! After all I've been through, I spawn once!"

"It is your fortune."

"Oh, please."

"It is better to have spawned and died

than to never have—"

"Tell it to the universe," I said as I curled into a semi-circle and exploded out of the kelp bed.

I WOKE UP WET AND COLD, SHAKEN AND DISTURBED.

To spawn or not to spawn. That was the question. I'd suffered the claws and talons of outrageous fortune and I'd fought against a sea of troubles. But no, the universe wanted more gifts. And what do you give the universe? The answer, it seemed, was floating in the stream. You give the universe whatever it wants.

Now I was to spawn, to die: to die,

perchance…to what?

I stewed most of the morning in a stretch of slack water near the entrance to Chilkat Lake. Revelations swirled around me like an eddy. Of course I'd never met a salmon that had spawned. And no wonder the support group, Salmon and Orphans, was so popular.

I watched school after school of smolts singing and playing on the first leg of their odyssey. Who among them would be the chosen? I watched the best of my generation drag their tired, disfigured bodies up the river. How many of their friends had died?

As the steady torrent of young smolts rushed past me and the elders fought their last battle, suddenly it all became clear. I was part of a continuous cycle of young and old, birth and death. I realized how foolish it was of me to fight the flow. I was one of the elite. I had seen the world and lived to come home, the last surviving member of my family.

"You are one of the chosen."

The pull of instinct, faster than thought, washed over me. I burst out of the water, my wasted body invigorated with purpose. I played the current as if I was a smolt again. I rounded the bend into Chilkat Lake and bumped a couple of fellow Sockeyes out of the way.

"Sorry, boys, I'm on a mission."

I scooted over the lakebed and there I was, in the Spawning Ground. As far as I could see, red bodies and green heads frolicked together in pairs while bitter bachelors fought to break up happy couples.

"Over here, Red."

It was Ova. She was digging the perfect redd near the shore of the lake.

"You're just in time, honey," she said, giving me a big wet kiss while putting the finishing touches on the redd, testing its depth with her anal fin.

"Timing's everything," I said, admiring the green hue of her head.

I was nibbling her ear when a male Sockeye swam by and bumped us. I snapped at him, sinking my teeth into his tail.

"You want a piece of me?!" I growled at him, spitting out a chunk of his flesh. "You want a piece of me?!"

"Hey!" the male salmon said, slicing away from me while blood from his wound stained the clear water. "You've got a serious attitude there, buddy."

"Sorry about that, honey," I said, caressing one of her lateral lines with my snout, "now where were we?"

"That was cute," she said, giggling.

Ova winked at me and settled down into the redd, closed her eyes and ground her teeth. Her body shuddered and hundreds of transparent eggs began dropping into the gravel. I slid down beside her and fertilized the eggs as they piled up in the redd.

Afterwards we used our tails to lovingly tuck our eggs safely under the gravel. Then we nuzzled together.

"You know, Ova, we're two of the chosen."

"It's our fortune, Red. The Dolly Salmon told me that a long time ago."

"What?" I said, startled. "The Dolly Salmon appeared to you, too?"

"Shhh," Ova said as she put her tail over mine.

I rubbed her snout one last time. Then, feeling complete and fulfilled, I closed my eyes and let myself slip away into the late afternoon light.

BOUDELANG PRESS ORDER FORM

NAME_____

STREET_____

CITY_____STATE_____ZIP_____

Add $1 for shipping on individual book orders. For 3 or more books, add a flat $3.

	mrs. claus			TOTAL
Quantity	_____		x $7=	_____
Coffee	cat	eagle		
_____	____	____	x $5=	_____
salmon	bear			
_____	____		x $5=	_____
Shipping			+	_____
			TOTAL DUE =	_____

__ **MASTERCARD** __ **VISA** __ **CHECK**

CARD #_____

EXP. DATE_____

PRINT NAME AS SHOWN ON CARD

_____

Please make checks payable to:

   BOUDELANG PRESS

   P.O Box 3005, Venice, CA 90291-9998

Questions? Please call 310.712.5606 or e-mail us at BOUDELANG@aol.com. Please visit our website www.boudelang.com.

Tom Lang lives in Venice, California. He has written for newspapers, magazines and the television and movie industry. Lang spends his summers working in Haines, Alaska as a river guide and lecturer at the Southeast Alaska Chilkat Bald Eagle Preserve, site of the largest gathering of American bald eagles in the world. Lang also reads and speaks at bookstores, libraries and colleges across the country.

Mr. Lang can be reached at (310) 712-5606, or e-mail at BOUDELANG@aol.com.